YES, I LOVE CATS!

This book belongs to:

Irene Hardy

I love cats!
White cats,

Black cats,

Begging-for-a-snack-cats,

Yes, I love cats!

I love cats!
Friendly cats,

Aloof cats,

Prowling-on-the-roof cats,

Yes, I love cats!

I love cats!
Hungry cats,

Well-fed cats,

Playing-on-my-bed cats,

Yes, I love cats!

I love cats!
Farmyard cats,

City cats,

Watchful little kitty-cats,

Yes, I love cats!

I love cats!
Lazy cats,

Active cats,

Powerfully attractive cats,

Yes, I love cats!

I love cats!
Tender cats,

Rough cats,

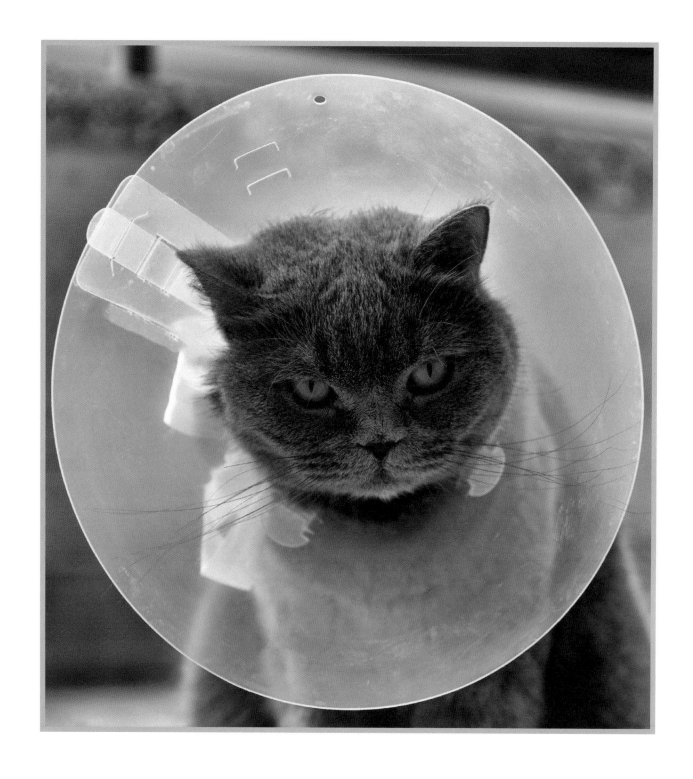

Lucky-they-are-tough cats,

Yes, I love cats!

I love cats!
Shy cats,

Bold cats,

Gently-growing-old cats,

Yes, I love cats!

I love cats!
Playful cats,

Intense cats,

Jumping-on-the-fence cats,

Yes, I love cats!

I love cats!
Skipper cats,

Shore cats,

Waiting-by-my-door cats,

Yes, I love cats!

Yes, I REALLY love cats!

REALLY, REALLY love cats!

Thanks for reading!

Images thanks to Deposit Photos: Elenakirey, lifeonwhite, denisovd, alexroz, mrdoomits,
snb2087, ampack, Kvitkanastroyu, belchonock, belchonock, TanyaTerekhina, AnmFoto, Mny-Jhee, okiepony,
Ulianna, esbenklinker, RenataA, maugli, annanahabed, elitravo, Chirtsova, milva_El, krappweis, zebuay,
kryzhov, sasamihajlovic, PantherMediaSeller, sjallenphoto, grase, 5seconds, aquamila, belovodchenko,
PrystaiSteffus, simfalex2, V.Sonnek.seznam.cz, alenka2194, Ulianna, VeronArt1, oksun70,
and also to Zantroke font from Gluk.

Printed in Great Britain
by Amazon

13616901R00025